Licensed exclusively to Top That Publishing Ltd
Tide Mill Way, Woodbridge, Suffolk, IP12 1AP, UK
www.topthatpublishing.com
Copyright © 2018 Tide Mill Media
All rights reserved
0 2 4 6 8 9 7 5 3 1
Manufactured in China

Written by Oakley Graham
Illustrated by Nina Caniac

ISBN 978-1-78445-248-3

A catalogue record for this book is available from the British Library

Shiver Me Timbers!

Written by Oakley Graham
Illustrated by Nina Caniac

This is the tale of a fearsome pirate crew,
They'll shiver your timbers with the things they do!
You're sure to walk the plank if you step out of line,
And singing on Sunday is a punishable crime!

Oh, the ocean waves may roll,
And the stormy winds may blow,
It's a life at sea for me ...
Yo ho ho!

Let's meet Captain Black,
he commands the pirate ship,
He's tall, lean and mean

and he likes to use his whip!

CRACK!

In place of his left hand
is a giant, pointy hook,

And he's missing his right leg
that a tiger shark once took.

Oh, the ocean waves may roll,
And the stormy winds may blow,
It's a life at sea for me ...

Yo ho ho!

The pirate ship set sail in the middle of November,
Across the stormy seas the buccaneers did venture.

Navigating by the stars under the light of a full moon,
Battling against the waves, whipped up by a typhoon.

Oh, the ocean waves may roll,
And the stormy winds may blow,
It's a life at sea for me ...

Yo ho ho!

Captain Black was very greedy,
he loved gold doubloons,
And if anyone
was mean to him,
they ended up
marooned.

The captain had a map
which led to lots
of buried treasure,
Counting all his riches
was this pirate's greatest
pleasure.

Oh, the ocean waves may roll,
And the stormy winds may blow,
It's a life at sea for me ...

Yo ho ho!

So you want to be a pirate?
It's not like it seems in books,
And if the navy catches you,
You'll be treated like a crook!

There's lots to do on board
and you'd better have sea legs,

Mending sails,

hoisting rigging

and scrubbing dirty decks.

Oh, the ocean waves may roll,
And the stormy winds may blow,
It's a life at sea for me ...

Yo ho ho!

When you're out at sea,
You often see some funny things,
Mermaids out on jagged rocks
and fish that fly
           with wings.

Ahoy!

It may be a surprise to you
that ships don't have a loo,
And that pirates lean overboard
when they have a poo!

SPLISH!

SPLASH!

SPLOSH!

POOP
DECK

Oh, the ocean waves may roll,
And the stormy winds may blow,
It's a life at sea for me ...
Yo ho ho!

DIDDLE-DI-DEE! DIDDLE-DI-DEE!

The pirates danced with glee
as they neared their destination,
Just off the Spanish coast of Main,
on a colony plantation.
The crew thought they'd made it,
when a shout came from the deck,

'An angry octopus has got
its tentacles around my neck!'

Oh, the ocean waves may roll,
And the stormy winds may blow,
It's a life at sea for me ...

Yo ho ho!

The octopus was enormous,
it reached right around the ship,
The brave pirates tried to fight it,
but the ship was firmly in its grip.

Then Captain Black stepped up
and hit it with his hook,
He knew he was in trouble
from the octopus' angry look!

Oh, the ocean waves may roll,
And the stormy winds may blow,
It's a life at sea for me ...
Yo ho ho!

The octopus began to dive, holding tight the pirate ship,
The captain tried to stop it, by using his trusty whip.

But the ship went down,
and this news may truly shock yer',
Captain Black now counts his treasure
down in Davy Jones' locker!

Oh, the ocean waves may roll,
And the stormy winds may blow,
It's a life at sea for me ...

Yo ho ho!

But that's not the end of the story, as some of the crew escaped,

They surfed ashore on bits of wood and on golden dinner plates.

They reached the treasure island
and met a friendly local tribe,
Then stayed on the island
using the treasure
as a bribe!

Oh, the ocean waves may roll,
And the stormy winds may blow,
It's a life at sea for me ...
Yo ho ho!

PIRATE FACTS

A pirate is a person who commits a crime while at sea. The crimes could be anything, but usually involve robbery or violence. Arr!!

During the seventeenth and eighteenth centuries, thousands of men and women turned to piracy as a way to make a living. This period is often referred to as The Golden Age of Piracy.

Most pirates did not bury their treasure! The captain would usually divide the loot and share it with the crew when they reached land.

Pirates didn't live for very long!
The tough conditions at sea, fights and battles meant that even the most successful pirates only lasted two or three years.

Pirates didn't walk the plank! There were lots of other horrible punishments, like being whipped, but walking the plank was not one of them (a little white lie in the story!).

Not all pirates were men! There were fierce women pirates like Anne Bonny and Mary Read, who dressed as men to conceal their identity.

PIRATE FACTS

The famous Jolly Roger flag, with its black background and white skull and crossbones, was designed to scare people into surrendering without a fight. This flag was not used by all pirates, and many created their own equally scary designs!

Pirates believed that wearing earrings would improve their eyesight.

They also thought that whistling on a ship brought bad luck and turned the weather stormy.

The most successful pirate ever was probably Bartholomew Roberts, known as Black Bart. He captured around 400 ships in the 1720s.

One of the most infamous pirates on the high seas was Edward Teach — Blackbeard! After many years of piracy, he was eventually defeated in a sword fight by naval officer Robert Maynard, in 1718.

Port Royal in Jamaica was a famous meeting place for pirates. It was often known as the 'City of Sin'.